BrAiN BENDERS

SEEING IS BELIEVING

Thanks to the creative team:

Senior Editor: Alice Peebles

Designer: Bryony Anne Warren

and Collaborate Agency

★

First published in Great Britain in 2015 by
Hungry Tomato Ltd
PO Box 181
Edenbridge
Kent, TN8 9DP

★

A CIP catalogue record for this book is available from the British Library.

ISBN 978-1-910684-054

Printed and bound in China

★

Discover more at www.hungrytomato.com

SEEING IS
BELIEVING

by Dr. Gareth Moore

HUNGRY
TOMATO™

Contents

Seeing is Believing

Can you believe your eyes? Normally you can, but there are times when they'll lie to you! Get ready to be amazed, astounded and appalled by just how confused your brain can get! Prepare for patterns that move, colours that change and objects that alter their size.

Negative image

Look at some of the red dots in this box, and move your eyes around from dot to dot. What do you see? You should see not just the red dots, but also ghostly after-images. These linger behind in your eyes and appear as extra, bright dots in the empty spaces. They might also be light blue in colour.

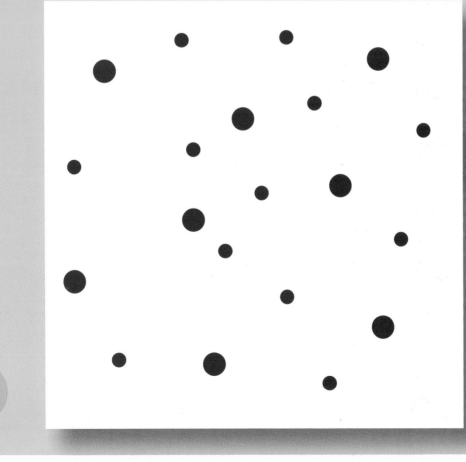

Need help with answering these questions? Turn to pages 26 to 29 for helpful tips.

Introducing Illusions

Can you always believe your eyes? Sometimes they have trouble making sense of what they're seeing – as you're about to find out!

1 Moving around

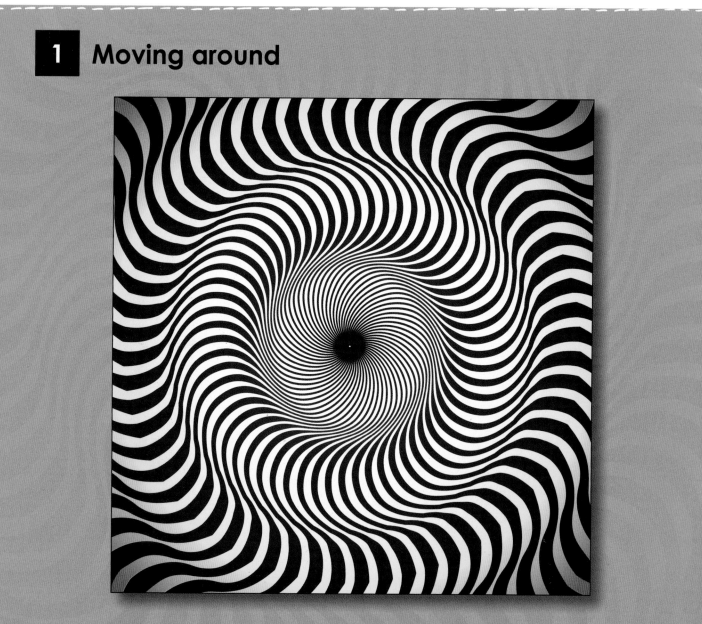

Hold the book quite close to your face and look at the centre of this pattern. Now slowly move the book away from you, while still looking at the centre. The different curves start to swirl around, as if they were moving on the page – amazing!

2 Parallel problem

These blue and orange lines look as if they get further apart or closer together as they run across the page, but do they really? Test this out by using a ruler to measure the distance between an orange and a blue line at the top of the picture, and again at the bottom.

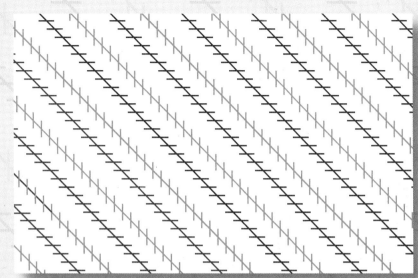

3 Lining up

If this white line were to continue in the same direction, which of the coloured lines would it meet up with? Have a guess using just your eyes, then find out the answer by using a ruler. Were you correct?

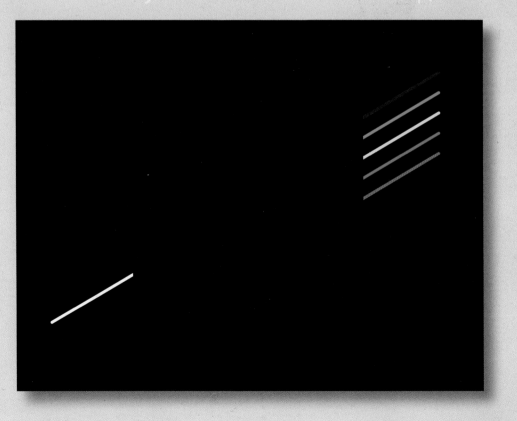

Need help with answering these questions? Turn to pages 26 to 29 for helpful tips.

Misleading Measurements

When you look at two different objects, can you always tell which is larger and which is smaller? Are you sure? The optical illusions on this page might surprise you!

1 Circle size

Which of these two green circles is larger? Or are they both the same size? Take a look first, then, once you've decided, measure them.

2 Rectangle comparison

Which of the three green rectangles is exactly the same size as the vertical yellow rectangle? Again, decide first, then measure them.

3 Table-top teaser

If you look at these red table tops, they seem to be very different shapes – but would you believe that they are in fact identical? They are both exactly the same parallelogram. See if you can confirm this by using a ruler. It's surprising, isn't it?

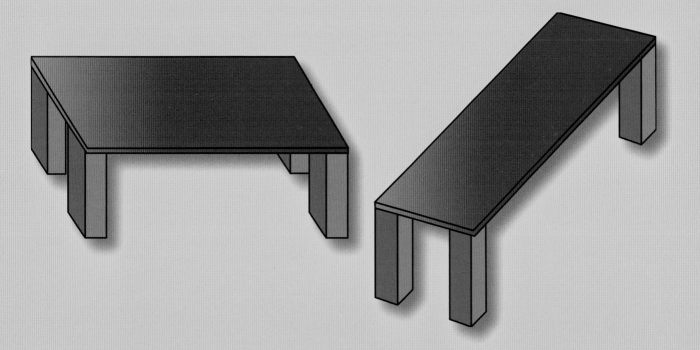

4 Pointing apart

Which pair of arrow points do you think is further apart – the left-hand and middle ones or the middle and right-hand ones?

Need help with answering these questions? Turn to pages 26 to 29 for helpful tips.

9

Distance-Illusions

Your brain uses your two eyes to work out how far away different objects are. It does this by comparing the view from one eye with the view from the other. But your brain also uses other cues to help it decide relative distances. The illusions on this page demonstrate some of the visual decoding techniques that you use every day without realizing!

1 Bowling balls

Look at these two blue bowling balls. Does the one at the top look larger? Try measuring them both to find out for sure.

2 Railway line

There are two wide metallic bars on top of these railway tracks, but the one at the top looks much larger than the one at the bottom. Measure them both to find out if all is as it seems.

3 Salt and pepper

This photograph appears to be of one large and one small pepper pot, but it's actually two pots of exactly the same size. The picture hasn't been modified since it was taken, so can you work out how the photographer made them look different sizes?

Need help with answering these questions? Turn to pages 26 to 29 for helpful tips.

Two-in-One Illusions

Seeing is believing, but what if you can see things that aren't even there? Your eyes are very good at noticing familiar patterns, so sometimes even empty areas can look like objects. Your brain is also great at spotting faces, which is why you can sometimes see what looks like a face on the surface of the moon!

1 Face the vase

What do you see here? Is it a vase? Or is it two people looking at each other?

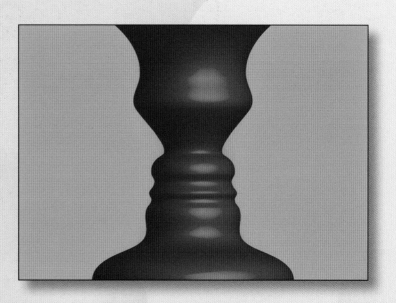

2 Hair or no hair?

Is this a man with a moustache and lots of hair?

Or is it a bald man with a beard – can you find him, too?

3 Pointing both ways

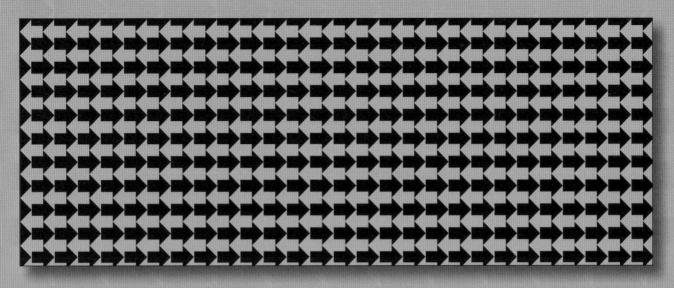

Do you see all orange arrows facing to the left, or all blue arrows facing to the right?

4 Cola or glasses?

Is this a few shelves of glasses, or a collection of cola bottles?

Need help with answering these questions? Turn to pages 26 to 29 for helpful tips.

Context Illusions

How you see an object in the real world depends not just on the object itself, but also on the appearance of everything around it. The illusions on these pages demonstrate this in three different ways.

1 White out

Looking at this picture at normal reading distance, you see a swirl of white lines heading off into blackness.

But focus on the centre of the picture, then slowly move the page closer, and something strange happens.

The white area in the centre expands, becoming both larger and brighter.

2 Whiter than white

The white square in the centre of each of these black squares appears to be glowing a much brighter white than the rest of the paper. But can that really be true?

3 Side by side

The path on the right of this picture seems to head off at a very different angle from the path on the left.

Or is this just an optical illusion, perhaps?

Need help with answering these questions? Turn to pages 26 to 29 for helpful tips.

Colour Perception

We all know that colours look very different at night from during the day, and have you ever noticed how different indoor lights can have a big effect on what a colour looks like? It's not just the type of light bulb in a lamp that changes a colour, though. Did you know that other nearby colours can also influence how you see light, shade and colour?

1 Grey areas

Look at these columns of grey discs. There appear to be two different shades of grey: light grey and dark grey. But is that really true? Are you sure?

2 Shades of colour

There seem to be three different shades of these four different colours here, but in fact something strange is happening.

The black and white bars are influencing your colour perception. Take a closer look and see if you can work out what's going on!

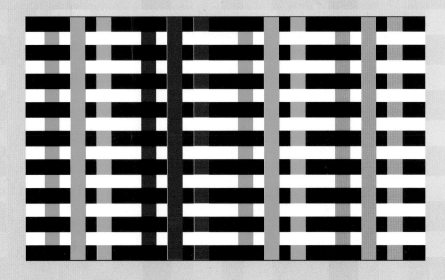

3 Coloured lights

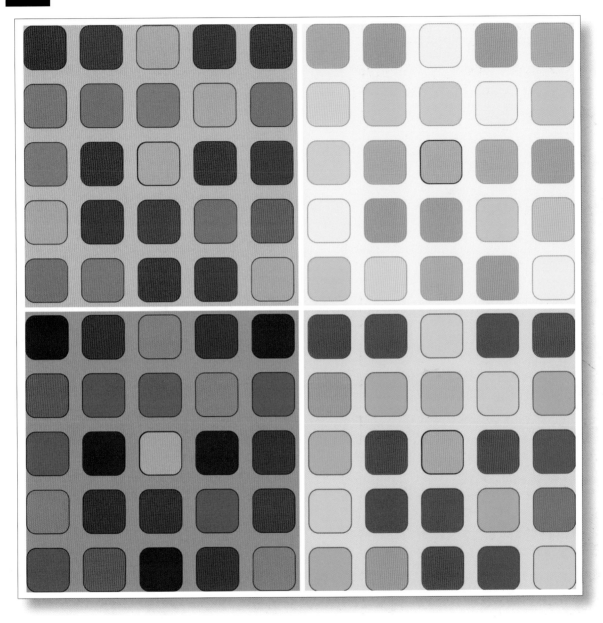

Look at the centre tile in each of these four coloured areas. In the top left picture the centre tile appears pale green, and in the top right picture it looks pale blue. In the bottom left picture it seems to be yellow, and in the bottom right picture it looks like a pale purple colour. It seems obvious that the colour of this tile varies, so this must be correct. Or is it?

Try comparing each of these centre tiles with this single grey tile. Surely they can't all be the same colour ... or can they?

Need help with answering these questions? Turn to pages 26 to 29 for helpful tips.

Colour Shifts

Things that you think you can see probably often surprise you, because they turn out to be figments of your imagination. You can also see imagined details even with simple shapes, as the illusions on these pages show. You'll find that your eyes can choose to hide details from you that really are there, too!

1 Colour flood

Take a look at this shape, and compare the paper inside this shape with the paper just outside the shape. Does the paper in the centre look a slightly different shade from what you see outside the shape?

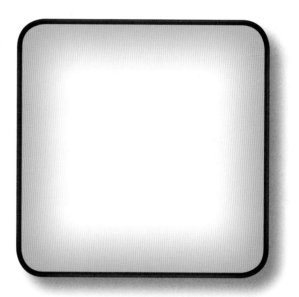

2 Boundary issues

Look at this green circle with a black cross on it. Does it look exactly the same shade of green all over the circle? Are you sure?

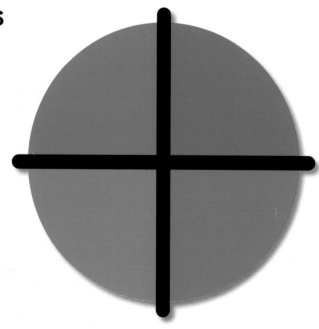

3 Simulating shapes

Do you see a pale orange square in the centre of this picture?

Does the paper there look a slightly different colour?

And can you even see some of the edges of that square?

How about these green circles? Some parts are missing, but can you see a bright white hexagon in the middle?

You might even see a three-dimensional cube, too, if your brain is really creative!

Look at these blue circles, each with a quarter coloured red. Can you also see a red square on the paper between them?

Need help with answering these questions? Turn to pages 26 to 29 for helpful tips.

Inversion Illusions

Have you ever looked at a bright light and found that your eyes didn't work so well afterwards? You see a ghostly image of the bright light, like a large spot on your vision. The brighter the light and the longer you look at it, the stronger the effect. If you stare at a really bright light, like the sun, you can damage your eyesight permanently – so never look directly at the sun!

It's not just bright lights that can cause a ghostly image. Looking at the same image for a long time, without moving your eyes, can do the same. In both cases, your eyes have received such a strong visual impression that it takes them a while to forget about it. What you see is the 'opposite' of the previous image, which is why a bright white light becomes a black spot in your vision.

1 Target rings

Stare into the centre of this set of circles for 10 seconds, then look away at a white wall or ceiling. What do you see?

You should see a floating set of circles, similar to this image. When you see the floating circles, stare right into the centre of them. This will strengthen the effect, and after a second or two you will see the whole image even more clearly.

Did you notice that the centre circle is now empty? It isn't black, like in the picture. This is because you are seeing an **inverted** version of the picture, where white becomes black and black becomes white.

2 | Traffic lights

The same effect also works in colour. Try staring at the centre circle in this set of three for 20 seconds, then look away at a distant white surface. What do you see?

Can you see different colours appearing? You should be able to see the three colours of traffic lights – red at the top, amber or yellow in the middle, and green at the bottom.

If you only see one or two of these colours, that's OK too.

3 | Colouring transmission

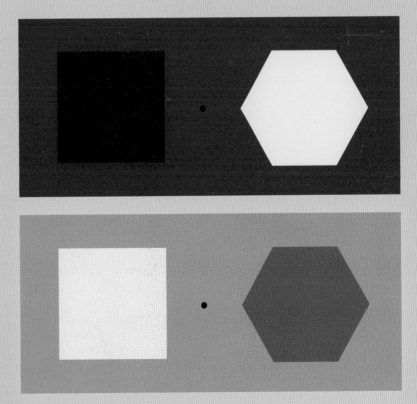

Stare at the black dot in the centre of the upper colour image for 20 seconds. Then look immediately at the black dot in the centre of the grey image directly below. Try to do this without blinking!

What do you see? Does the grey image now appear in colour? What colour is the background, and each of the shapes? They are not the same as in the upper image. The effect vanishes if you blink or take too long to move your eyes to the second black dot, so try again if you don't see it the first time!

Need help with answering these questions? Turn to pages 26 to 29 for helpful tips.

21

Grid Illusions

All the illusions in this book involve fairly simple drawings that nonetheless often result in far-from-simple visual effects. The drawings on this page are simpler still – little more than regular grids, just like you would find on a piece of graph paper!

1 Shape in the hole

This simple square grid has gaps where the lines would otherwise cross.

There's nothing special about these gaps – but there appears to be a bright white circle in every one of them!

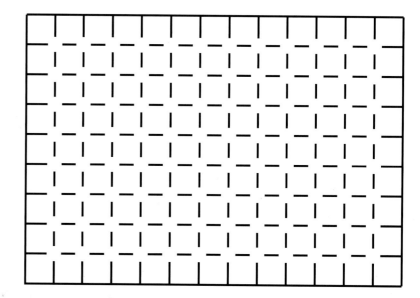

2 Coloured circles

In this picture the missing bits of the lines have been put back in, but they have been drawn in colour rather than black.

Amazingly, you can still see circles where the gaps were before, but now they take on the colour used to fill in the gaps!

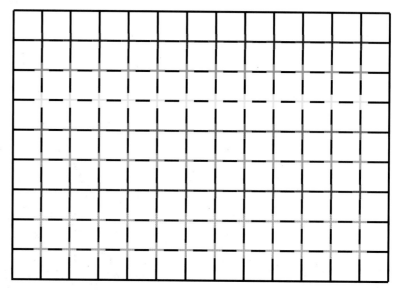

3 Ghostly dots

This very simple drawing of blue squares on a black background hides some ghostly grey dots. Look at any of the blue squares, then move your eyes to look at a different square. You will see ghostly grey dots flickering on the intersections between squares, just away from the centre of your vision.

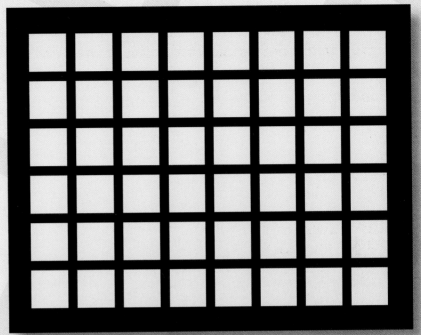

4 More ghostly dots

This picture shows a regular grid of green lines on a black background. Where the grid lines intercept, a pale dot has been drawn.

That's all there is to the picture, and yet as you move your eyes around it, you will see black dots flashing randomly on and off on top of each of the pale dots!

Need help with answering these questions? Turn to pages 26 to 29 for helpful tips.

Persistence of Vision

Your eyes can carry on responding to what they've seen for a short period of time, even after the image itself has gone. This effect is called "persistence of vision" and it's how film and television work. Those images aren't really moving but are just a lot of still images that change very quickly. Your eyes can also get tired, and stop telling you about things they think you already know.

1 Negative image

Just as you did on page 5, look at these yellow dots, then move your eyes around from dot to dot. What do you see now?

2 Fade to grey

Hold the book so this grey
circle fills most of your vision,
and stare at the centre,
making sure you don't
move your eyes away.

After just a second or two,
you should find that the
entire circle fades away,
until you can't see it at all!

Moving your eyes around
will make it appear again.

3 Vanishing colours

There are five brightly
coloured shapes in this
image. Hold the book
as close as you can
while still being able
to see them all. Now
focus on the orange
shape in the centre.
Stare into the middle
of it and you will find,
amazingly, that the
four other coloured
shapes vanish!

Keep staring and
eventually the
orange shape will
fade away, too.

Need help with answering these questions? Turn to pages 26 to 29 for helpful tips.

Helpful Tips

Page 5

Introduction

If you don't see this immediately, try looking at each dot for a bit longer.

Pages 6 – 7

Introducing Illusions

Moving around

Your eyes have trouble focusing so move around rapidly and create an impression of movement. The effect is less strong at the corners.

Parallel problem

Take two pieces of paper and arrange them like a letterbox, so that you can only see a small part of the image in between. Now slide your letterbox up and down the image. Do the lines still seem to move apart?

Lining up

Once you've made your mind up, rotate the book and look along the length of the white line. Do you still think the same?

Pages 8 – 9

Misleading Measurements

Circle size

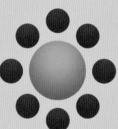

Similar objects are often similar sizes, so this illusion relies on your brain assuming that all of the red circles are related in size in some way. If you cover over the red circles, what do you think now?

Rectangle comparison

We're really bad at judging the heights of tall objects, as this illusion demonstrates. Try rotating the book as you concentrate on just the top two rectangles.

Table-top teaser

It's very hard to believe that the table tops might be the same. Try covering over the table legs, since these are giving you misleading information.

Pointing apart

Looking at the arrows, your brain assumes the centre points best describe their positions, but in this case it's the arrow tips that matter. Try covering over most of each arrow so that you can just see their tips.

Pages 10 – 11

Distance Illusions

Bowling balls

When something moves further away from you, it appears to get smaller. In this drawing we have simulated distance with the background, so try covering over as much of the grey shape as you can and looking just at the two balls.

Railway line

It looks like the railway line is heading off into the distance, so if this were a photograph you'd know that in real life the upper bar would have to be much bigger in order to appear the same size as the other. Try covering over some of the rails. What happens now?

Salt and pepper

The pepper pots really are the same size, and this is a real photograph. Think about what viewing angle you might need to photograph them from to get this result.

Pages 12 – 13 Two-in-One Illusions

Face the vase

This really is a picture of a vase, but the vase has been carefully designed to share its profile with a face.
By focusing on the orange area or the blue area you should be able to see either vase or faces, or even both at once!

Hair or no hair?

Did you find the bearded man? Have you tried looking at the picture from a different angle?

Pointing both ways

The gaps between the drawn arrows make identical arrow shapes pointing the opposite way. You can try drawing this yourself. Can you come up with other patterns that work like this?

Cola or glasses?

The gaps between the glasses really do look like shelves and bottles. What you see is up to you, although you probably saw the glasses first because they are shaded to look like real objects. But even with this visual cue, you can still see the bottles if you choose.

Pages 14 – 15 Context Illusions

White out

If you're having trouble seeing this, move the book towards you more slowly. Make sure you stay focused on the very centre of the image. As you change what you can see in your peripheral vision, so your vision adapts to the parts of the image it can still see.

Whiter than white

To find out if this is an illusion or not,  try hiding the black squares to see if they're causing the effect.

One way to do this is to take another piece of paper and cut a small hole in it. Lay it on the page and use the hole to look at different white parts of the picture.

Side by side

Try covering over one path, then covering over the other. Now what do you think?

Page 16

Colour Perception

Grey areas

Take a piece of paper and place it over the drawing. Now put a small x over a light grey circle, and another small x over a dark grey circle. Remove the paper and cut out a small hole at each x. Put the paper back in place and look through the holes – do they still look different shades of grey?

Shades of colour

Place two pieces of paper together so as to leave just a very narrow letterbox gap between them. Lay them on the page so that you can see just one of the black strips, revealing two shades of each colour. Do they still look like different shades? Now slide the pieces of paper down so that you can see just one of the white strips, again revealing two shades of each colour. Do they still look like different shades, too?

Page 17

Colour Perception

Coloured lights

This is a remarkable illusion, so it can be very hard to see it as it truly is. Make a small hole in a plain piece of paper and look through it at each of the centre tiles, as well as the single grey tile. Can you see that they are all the same colour?

Page 18

Colour Shifts

Colour flood

If you have trouble seeing this, try again later in different light.

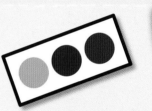

Boundary issues

One method to reveal this as a trick is to take a piece of paper and place the edge of the paper over one of the quarters of the circle. Colour part of the edge to match the green on the page as closely as you can, using coloured pencils or crayons. Now, move the paper edge over the other quarters in turn – do they all match the colour in the same way?

Page 19

Colour shifts

Simulating shapes

If you have trouble seeing these hidden shapes, try looking at the book in brighter light. They are much harder to see in low lighting.

Pages 20 – 21

Inversion Illusions

Target rings

If you don't see the floating circles then look at the picture for twice as long and in a brighter light, and work out where you will look afterwards in advance.

Traffic lights

If you don't see anything, try using a piece of bright white paper instead of a distant wall. If you just see a blur, focus directly on the centre of that ghostly image. This will help you see it more clearly.

Colour transmission

Make sure you only look at the black dots and nowhere else, and try very hard not to blink! If you still can't see it, try looking at the colour image for longer before you switch to the grey and white image.

Pages 22 – 23

Grid Illusions

Shape in the hole

To see the circles, try staring directly at the gaps.

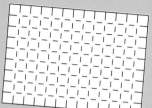

Coloured circles

Look directly at the yellow crosses, since they provide the most visual contrast with the black lines.

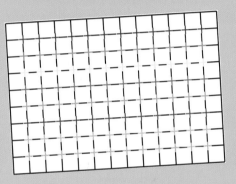

Ghostly dots

Look at a blue square and then gently relax your eyes. As you soften your focus, you should see the ghostly dots more clearly.

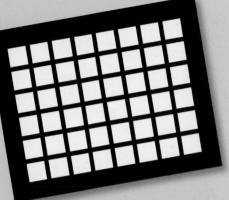

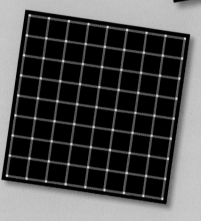

More ghostly dots

If you don't see these, then move your eyes around slightly more quickly, or look out of the corner of your eyes at the rest of the grid. You could also try holding the book a little closer to you.

Pages 24 – 25

Persistence of Vision

Negative image

You can still see this effect even if you don't look directly at the dots.

Try looking at the background in one place for a second or so, then shift your gaze to another part of the background.

Fade to grey

If you have trouble seeing this effect, try a brighter room and hold the book a little bit closer. If this still doesn't work, put the book down for a bit and try again later – maybe your eyes are getting too tired!

Vanishing colours

This effect works best when it fills your vision and is evenly lit, so make sure there are no shadows across the page and that you are holding the book as steadily as you can.

Answers

Page 7 Introducing Illusions

Parallel problem

The lines are all perfectly parallel, or in other words none of them get any closer together or further apart at any point in the picture. You can verify this with a ruler!

Lining up

The white line is pointing at the blue line. Most people think it is one of the lower lines instead.

Pages 10 – 11 Distance Illusions

Bowling balls

Both balls are identical in size. The illusion is caused because the upper part of the grey shape appears to be further away, so your brain is assuming that the upper ball must be larger than the lower ball. This is because the further away an object is, the smaller it appears to your eyes. Your brain automatically corrects for this, so you don't get confused by objects appearing to change size as you move around the world. In this case, the top of the shape isn't really further away from you, so your brain gets it wrong and tells you the upper ball is larger than it actually is.

Railway line

Both bars are identical in every way.

Salt and pepper

The pepper pots are arranged as in the photo below, but the image on the page was photographed level with the table top, so that one pot looks smaller than the other because it is further from the camera.

Pages 8 – 9 Misleading Measurements

Circle size

The green circles are exactly the same size.

Rectangle comparison

The yellow rectangle is the same size as the top green rectangle. Most people think it is the middle green rectangle.

Table top-teaser

The two table tops are identical in shape and size. You could trace one table top shape onto a piece of paper and lay it over the other one to prove it.

Pointing apart

The distance between each pair of arrow tips is identical, as a ruler will confirm.

Pages 12 – 13 Two-in-One Illusions

Face the vase

This vase is drawn so that its outline matches that of a face in profile, so even though it really is a picture of a vase, it's also perfectly normal to see two faces as well.

Hair or no hair?

Turn the page upside down to see the other man!

Pointing both ways

There is no correct answer to this – we could have drawn either set of arrows to produce this picture. What you see is up to you, and you will probably easily see either version.

Cola or glasses?

We drew the glasses first, but again there is no correct answer here. We designed the glasses to make the gaps look like bottles, so what you see is up to you – and you can almost certainly see both.

Page 15 **Context Illusions**

Whiter than white

The paper is the same shade of white in all places.

Side by side

Both paths are identical. In real life your view at any one time is always from the single fixed point of where you are. This means that if two separate paths looked identical in a photograph taken from that one position, they would be different in reality. Your clever brain applies this principle to the picture, but as it doesn't know the difference between a drawing and reality, you end up with confusing visual information.

Pages 20 – 21

Inversion Illusions

Target rings

The image should appear with black replacing white, and vice versa, when you see the ghostly image.

Traffic lights

The light blue spot appears red, the dark blue spot appears yellow/amber, and the purple spot appears green, just like a traffic light.

Colour transmission

You should see the following image:

Pages 16 – 17 **Colour Perception**

Grey areas

There is only one shade of grey here. Amazing, isn't it?

Shades of colour

There are only four different colours here. The darker and lighter versions of each colour are assumptions made by your brain based on the white and black strips that overlap them.

Pages 18 – 19

Colour Shifts

Colour flood

The paper in the centre of the shape is exactly the same colour as the paper just outside the shape.

Boundary issues

There are actually three different shades of green – the top right quarter is darkest and the bottom left quarter is lightest. The other two quarters are an in-between shade.

Page 22 **Grid Illusions**

Shape in the hole

There are no circles on the page, but there certainly appear to be!

Coloured lights

All the centre tiles are exactly the same colour as the separate grey tile. Your brain is "colour correcting" according to the surrounding image, which it thinks is lit by a different colour light in each case. To understand this, imagine how everything would look different if you had a red light bulb in a lamp instead of a white one. Your brain is assuming that something similar is happening here, and it's adapting so automatically to the different lighting situations that you are unable to "switch off" this behaviour!

Stimulating shapes

None of these shapes are really there, and the paper doesn't change colour. Nonetheless, the visual cues strongly suggest that they exist, and it's quite normal to see the paper as a slightly different colour.

Colouring circles

There are no circles, coloured or not, but your brain thinks there are.

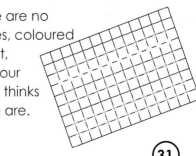

Index

About the Author

Dr. Gareth Moore is the author of a wide range of puzzle and brain-training books for both children and adults, including The Kids' Book of Puzzles, The Mammoth Book of Brain Games and The Rough Guide Book of Brain Training. He is also the founder of daily brain training site **www.BrainedUp.com**. He gained his Ph.D from Cambridge University (UK) in the field of computer speech recognition, teaching machines to understand spoken words.